gerald

finzi

Requiem da Camera

for baritone solo, small chorus (or SATB soli) & chamber orchestra,
with a completion by Christian Alexander

words by John Masefield, Thomas Hardy & Wilfrid Wilson Gibson

vocal score

BOOSEY & HAWKES

Boosey & Hawkes Music Publishers Ltd
www.boosey.com

Published by Boosey & Hawkes Music Publishers Ltd
Aldwych House
71–91 Aldwych
London
WC2B 4HN

www.boosey.com

ISMN 979-0-060-12681-9
ISMN 978-0-85162-922-3

Second impression 2014

Printed in the EU by Halstan

Music origination by New Notations London

CONTENTS

Requiem da Camera

The Finzi Trust exists to support the promotion of the music of Gerald Finzi.
For further information visit www.geraldfinzi.org or www.boosey.com

PREFACE

Finzi's *Requiem da Camera*, scored for baritone, mixed chorus and small orchestra, was his first attempt at composing an extended work comprising several movements. Together with the first short orchestral essay, *A Severn Rhapsody*, he designated the two works as his opus 3 under the title of *English Pastorals and Elegies*. The wellspring of its composition was the death, during active service in 1918, of his first composition teacher, Ernest Farrar. Finzi was shattered; more than just a teacher, Farrar had been an inspirational mentor and friend to the shy teenager.

The *Requiem*'s musical origins are traced to Finzi's 1923 setting of Thomas Hardy's *In Time of 'The Breaking of Nations'* (with its well-known opening lines 'Only a man harrowing clods'), for male voices and piano. This would become the third movement of the *Requiem da Camera*, to which would be added in the following year two further settings of poetry written during the First World War – verses from John Masefield's *August, 1914*, and W W Gibson's 'Lament', from *Whin* – forming the second and fourth movements respectively, the whole being prefaced by an orchestral prelude. Finzi had no success in his attempts to get the work published and at some point during the 1930s it seems he decided the Hardy setting was unsatisfactory since he wrote an entirely new version for baritone solo, conceived for orchestral accompaniment (although this was only partially completed).

Apart from its specific commemoration of his beloved teacher and, by extension, other fallen musicians such as George Butterworth, the work may be viewed as a metaphor – the permanence of the land, and a centuries-old pattern of rural life following the rhythm of the turning seasons, contrasted with the violent havoc and destructive dislocation wrought by war, as encapsulated by Hardy in the second verse of the poem Finzi set: 'Yet this will go onward the same/Though Dynasties pass'. Overall, the description by Philip Thomas (who prepared an edition of the work in 1984) sums up the work succinctly: 'Despite its elegiac stillness, Finzi's *Requiem* is a protest – a desperate cry for some certainty in a faithless world'.

Finzi binds his work together with a motif heard at the opening of the prelude which also includes overt references to Butterworth's song 'Loveliest of Trees' from his settings of A E Housman's *A Shropshire Lad*. In the oboe's poignant solo towards the end, Finzi weaves in allusions to *The Last Post*, which will recur hauntingly at the end of the work played by the flute. Apart from the final Hardy setting, Finzi's voice for the majority of the work is still as if in a chrysalis, yet there are pointers to the mature composer – the use of Bachian counterpoint, dissonant chromatic clashes between sharp and flat notes for vivid word-painting, and the slow, march-like tread of descending bass lines.

The only part of the *Requiem da Camera* to be performed during Finzi's lifetime was the Prelude, played by the London Chamber Orchestra, conducted by Anthony Bernard, on 1 December 1925 at Court House, Marylebone Lane, London, under the auspices of the British Music Society. Philip Thomas's edition of the full work, with his completed orchestration of the third movement, was first performed on 7 June 1990, at Christ Church, Spitalfields, London, with Stephen Varcoe, baritone, the BBC Northern Singers and the City of London Sinfonia, conducted by Richard Hickox.

The present edition and completion by Christian Alexander was first performed on 1 December 2013 at St Scholastica's Chapel, Glebe NSW, Australia, by Coro Innominata, conducted by David Taylor.

Andrew Burn, 2013

EDITORIAL NOTE

In preparing this new performing edition of Finzi's *Requiem da Camera* I made use of the following sources:

(1) Finzi's handwritten score of movements I, II and IV (facsimile)
(2) Finzi's incomplete score of movement III (facsimile: Bodleian Library, MS. Mus. b. 33, fols 108–115)
(3) an earlier handwritten setting by Finzi of *In Time of 'The Breaking of Nations'* for voice and piano (facsimile: Bodleian Library, MS. Mus. b. 33, fols 106–107)
(4) handwritten arrangement of *Prelude (Requiem da Camera)* for piano duet by Howard Ferguson (in copyist's hand, facsimile)
(5) handwritten vocal score with piano reduction, movements II, III and IV (in copyist's hand, facsimile)

Although only the opening Prelude was performed in Finzi's lifetime, the whole work was performed and recorded in the 1984 edition by Philip Thomas. Finzi completed the scoring of movements I, II and IV, and only very minor editorial work was required in these sections of *Requiem da Camera* in preparing this edition. One such amendment was in the second movement, bar 58 (the bar before letter D): the F-flat in Finzi's score seems to be an error, and was changed to an F-natural. It should also be noted that in bar 69 of the second movement the tenors sing F-sharp as the last note of beat 4, whereas Philip Thomas's edition has F-natural (as does Richard Hickox's recording of that edition). Finzi's handwritten score has a 'cut and paste' that obliterates the key signature in the tenor part only on that particular page, and no natural sign is inserted before the note in question. In the handwritten vocal score the note is unequivocally F-sharp. I therefore do not believe that it was Finzi's intention to naturalise the F-sharp.

Comparatively more editorial input was necessary in order to prepare the third movement (*In Time of 'The Breaking of Nations'*) for performance. The first twenty bars of the third movement were completed by Finzi in full score, although some editorial input was required here too (to my mind, Finzi undoubtedly would have made alterations had he needed to prepare the music for a performance); these include the insertion of dynamic markings, phrasing, clarification of *divisi* markings in the strings, and adding missing accidentals. I also added two notes to the horn part in bar 8, in order to correct a mistake in the second violin part of Finzi's score.

Far more editorial input was required from bar 21 to the end of the third movement in order to bring the music to a completed form. That said, enough information exists in Finzi's unfinished score (particularly when viewed alongside his more precise piano reduction) to provide strong clues as to the composer's intentions, and I have kept in place virtually everything from the incomplete full score, merely fleshing it out as I hope Finzi might have done.

Although it is stated in my edition that the vocal part of *Requiem da Camera* is for four solo voices or small chorus it should be noted that in the handwritten vocal score the following instruction is given: 'The vocal part is for 4 soloists: It can also be performed by a small equal chorus of not more than 4 to a line. In this case it wd be advisable to add to the strings a maximum of 4.4.3.3.2 and less in proportion to a smaller chorus. (The 2nd double-bass shd not be used with anything less than the maximum.)'

Christian Alexander, May 2013

PRÉFACE

Le *Requiem da Camera* de Finzi, pour baryton, chœur mixte et petit orchestre, constitue son premier essai de composition d'une œuvre d'envergure en plusieurs mouvements. Lui adjoignant sa première brève page orchestrale, *A Severn Rhapsody*, Finzi rassembla les deux œuvres sous le numéro d'opus 3 qu'il intitula *English Pastorals and Elegies*. L'origine de la composition du *Requiem* remonte à la mort, sous les drapeaux en 1918, de son premier professeur de composition Ernest Farrar, qui fut, plus qu'un simple maître, un mentor inspiré et un ami de Finzi l'adolescent timide, bouleversé par sa disparition.

Les prémices musicales du *Requiem da Camera* de Finzi remontent à sa mise en musique réalisée en 1923, pour voix d'hommes et piano, du poème de Thomas Hardy *In Time of 'The Breaking of Nations'* (et de son célèbre premier vers «*Only a man harrowing clods*») qui deviendra le troisième mouvement de l'œuvre. S'y ajouteront l'année suivante deux autres mises en musique de poèmes écrits pendant la première guerre mondiale : extraits d'*August, 1914* de John Masefield et la «Lamentation» extraite de *Whin* de W W Gibson, qui forment respectivement les deuxième et quatrième mouvements de l'œuvre et sont précédés d'un prélude orchestral. Finzi ne parvint pas à faire publier son œuvre et il semble qu'au cours des années 1930, insatisfait de sa mise en musique du poème de Hardy, il en composa une version entièrement nouvelle pour baryton seul et un accompagnement orchestral qui ne fut que partiellement achevé.

Outre l'hommage spécifique à son cher maître et, par extension, à d'autres musiciens morts au combat comme George Butterworth, cette œuvre peut être considérée comme la métaphore de la permanence de la terre et du cycle séculaire de la vie rurale au rythme des saisons en contraste avec le violent bouleversement et la dislocation destructrice apportés par la guerre, ainsi que l'exprime le deuxième vers du poème de Finzi «*Yet this will go onward the same / Though Dynasties pass*». De façon générale, la description de Philip Thomas (qui réalisa une édition de l'œuvre en 1984) résume justement l'œuvre : «Malgré sa paix élégiaque, le *Requiem* de Finzi est une protestation, un cri désespéré pour une forme de certitude dans un monde sans foi.»

Finzi unifie son œuvre par un motif apparu au début du prélude contenant des références identifiables à la mélodie de Butterworth *Loveliest of Trees* (*Les plus jolis des arbres*) extraite de la mise en musique de ce dernier de *A Shropshire Lad* (*Un gars du Shropshire*) d'A E Housman. Dans le solo poignant de la fin du prélude, Finzi insère des allusions à la sonnerie en hommage aux soldats disparus, *The Last Post*, qui reviendront obsessionnellement jouées à la flûte vers la fin de l'œuvre. A l'exception de la mise en musique finale du poème de Hardy, l'expression de Finzi dans l'ensemble de l'œuvre apparaît encore comme une chrysalide portant les signes annonciateurs de la maturité à venir du compositeur, tels que le contrepoint à la manière de Bach, les frottements chromatiques dissonants entre notes diésées et bémolisées animant la nature descriptive du discours et la lente progression en forme de marche des lignes de basse descendantes.

Seul le prélude du *Requiem da Camera* fut exécuté du vivant de Finzi par le London Chamber Orchestra sous la direction d'Anthony Bernard, le 1er décembre 1925, à Londres (salle du Court House, Marylebone Lane) sous le patronage de la British Music Society. L'œuvre complète, selon l'édition réalisée par Philip Thomas incluant l'achèvement de l'orchestration du troisième mouvement, fut donnée le 7 juin 1990 à Londres, à la Christ Church de Spitafields, avec le baryton Stephen Varcoe, les BBC Northern Singers et le City of London Sinfonia sous la baguette de Richard Hickox.

Notre édition, réalisée et complétée par Christian Alexander, fit l'objet d'une exécution le 1er décembre 2013 en la chapelle St Scholastica, Glebe NSW (Australie), par le Coro Innominata sous la direction de David Taylor.

Andrew Burn, 2013

COMMENTAIRE ÉDITORIAL

Pour la préparation de cette nouvelle édition du *Requiem da Camera* de Finzi en vue de son exécution, j'ai consulté les sources suivantes :

(1) manuscrit autographe de la partition de Finzi des mouvements I, II et IV (facsimilé)

(2) partition autographe incomplète de Finzi du mouvement III (facsimilé à la Bodleian Library, 108–115)

(3) manuscrit autographe plus ancien de Finzi de sa mise en musique de *In Time of 'The Breaking of Nations'* pour voix et piano (facsimilé à la Bodleian Library, MS. Mus. B. 33, pp 106–107)

(4) arrangement manuscrit pour piano à quatre mains du *Prélude (Requiem da Camera)* réalisé par Howard Ferguson (copie de copiste, facsimilé)

(5) manuscrit de la partition avec réduction pour piano des mouvements II, III et IV (copie de copiste, facsimilé)

Seul le *Prélude* initial fut créé du vivant de Finzi, l'œuvre intégrale ayant été exécutée et enregistrée plus tard selon l'édition de 1984 complétée et réalisée par Philip Thomas. Finzi ayant achevé l'instrumentation des mouvements I, II et IV, très peu de corrections de détail furent nécessaires dans ces parties lors de ma préparation de cette édition. Parmi ces changements figure, dans le deuxième mouvement, mesure 58 (une mesure avant D), la rectification du *fa* bémol de la partition de Finzi, qui semble être une erreur, en *fa* naturel. Il est également à noter qu'à la mesure 69 du deuxième mouvement, les ténors chantent un *fa* dièse sur la dernière note du 4ème temps, là où l'édition de Philip Thomas indique un *fa* naturel (repris par l'enregistrement de Richard Hickox de cette même édition). Or la partition manuscrite de Finzi présente un «collage» qui cache l'armure de la clef de la partie de ténor sur cette page précise mais aucun signe bécarre de figure devant la note en question. La partition vocale manuscrite indique un *fa* dièse sans équivoque possible. Je ne pense donc pas que l'intention de Finzi fût de modifier le *fa* dièse pour un *fa* bécarre.

En revanche, un travail éditorial plus approfondi fut nécessaire à l'édition du troisième mouvement (*In Time of 'The Breaking of Nations'*) afin de rendre possible son exécution. La partition complète des vingt premières mesures du troisième mouvement fut achevée par Finzi, bien que quelques modifications y aient aussi été indispensables (Finzi aurait, à mon avis, sans aucun doute effectué ces changements s'il avait dû préparer la partition pour son exécution), parmi lesquelles l'insertion d'indications de nuances dynamiques, de phrasé, la clarification des indications de divisi des cordes et l'adjonction d'altérations accidentelles manquantes. J'ai également ajouté deux notes à la mesure 8 de la partie de cor afin de corriger une erreur figurant dans la partie de second violon de la partition de Finzi.

Une contribution éditoriale beaucoup plus importante fut indispensable de la mesure 21 à la fin du mouvement de manière à parachever l'œuvre. Toutefois, la partition inachevée de Finzi comporte assez d'informations (en particulier si on la compare à sa réduction pour piano plus précise) pour guider vers les intentions du compositeur. J'ai donc maintenu en place pratiquement tout les éléments de la partition inachevée que j'ai simplement enrichis comme, je l'espère, Finzi l'aurait fait.

La partie vocale de mon édition du *Requiem da Camera* requiert quatre voix solistes ou un petit chœur. Il est cependant à noter qu'apparaît la recommandation suivante sur la partition vocale manuscrite de Finzi : «La partie vocale est destinée à 4 solistes. Elle peut aussi être chantée par un petit chœur de voix égales ne comprenant pas plus de 4 exécutants par parties. Dans ce cas, il serait conseillé d'ajouter aux cordes un maximum de 4.4.3.3.2 ou moins en proportion d'un chœur plus réduit. (La deuxième contrebasse ne devrait être utilisée qu'avec un effectif maximal.)»

Christian Alexander, mai 2013
Traduction : Agnès Ausseur

VORBEMERKUNG

Finzis *Requiem da Camera* für Bariton, gemischten Chor und kleines Orchester war der erste Versuch des Komponisten, ein längeres Werk aus mehreren Sätzen zu schaffen. Er fasste dieses Werk mit der ersten, kurzen Orchesterdichtung *A Severn Rhapsody* (Eine Severn-Rhapsodie) unter dem Titel *English Pastorals and Elegies* (Englische Pastoralen und Elegien) zusammen und gab ihnen die Opuszahl 3. Mit der Schaffung des *Requiems* wollte Finzis dem für ihn erschütternden Tod seines ersten Kompositionslehrers, Ernest Farrar, gedenken, der 1918 an der Front gefallen war. Für den schüchternen Jugendlichen war Farrar nicht nur ein Lehrer, sondern auch ein inspirierender Mentor und Freund gewesen.

Musikalisch geht das *Requiem* auf Finzis Vertonung (1923) von Thomas Hardys *In Time of 'The Breaking of Nations'* (mit seinen wohlbekannten einleitenden Zeilen „Only a man harrowing clods") für Männerstimmen und Klavier zurück. Diese Vertonung sollte später den dritten Satz des *Requiems* bilden. 1924 fügte Finzi dem Satz zwei weitere Vertonungen von Lyrik hinzu. Die Texte dazu entstanden im Ersten Weltkrieg: Strophen aus John Masefields *August, 1914* und W. W. Gibsons „Lament" aus *Whin*. Deren Vertonungen bildeten den zweiten und vierten Satz des *Requiems*. Dem Ganzen wurde ein Orchestervorspiel vorangestellt. Finzis Versuche, das Werk bei einem Verleger unterzubringen, blieben erfolglos. Irgendwann in den 1930er Jahren scheint der Komponist die Hardyvertonung für unbefriedigend befunden zu haben, denn er komponierte eine völlig neue Fassung für Baritonsolisten, der von einem Orchester begleitet werden sollte (diese Fassung wurde allerdings nur teilweise abgeschlossen).

Neben der konkreten Würdigung des geliebten Lehrers und damit inbegriffen auch anderer gefallener Musiker wie z. B. George Butterworth lässt sich das Werk zudem als eine Metapher für die Unverwüstlichkeit der Erde und die jahrhundertealte, dem Rhythmus der wechselnden Jahreszeiten folgende Routine des Landlebens interpretieren. Im Gegensatz dazu stehen das gewaltsame Chaos und die zerstörerische Verirrung, die von Krieg verursacht werden. Diese Metapher hat Hardy besonders in der zweiten Strophe des von Finzi vertonten Gedichts zum Ausdruck gebracht: „Yet this will go onward the same/ Though Dynasties pass". Alles in allem fassen die Worte von Philip Thomas (der 1984 eine Ausgabe des Werkes vorbereitete) das Werk treffend zusammen: „Trotz seiner elegischen Ruhe ist Finzis *Requiem* ein Protest – ein verzweifelter Ruf nach etwas Sicherheit in einer Welt ohne Glauben."

Finzi schweißt das Werk mithilfe eines Motivs zusammen, das zu Beginn des Vorspiels zu hören ist. Das Vorspiel enthält auch deutliche Bezüge zu Butterworth' Lied „Loveliest of Trees" (Der entzückendste Baum), das in seiner Vertonung von A. E. Housmans *A Shropshire Lad* (Ein Bursche aus Shropshire) vorkommt. In dem wehmütigen Oboensolo gegen Ende des *Requiems* flicht Finzi Anspielungen an das zum Gedenken an die im Krieg gefallenen Soldaten des Commonwealth häufig gespielte militärische Hornsignal *The Last Post* (Der letzte Wachposten) ein. Unheimlich kehrt dieses Signal von der Flöte vorgetragen zum Schluss wieder. Wenn man einmal von der abschließenden Hardyvertonung absieht, klingt Finzis Stimme im Großteil des Werkes zurückhaltend, wie eingeschlossen in einem Kokon. Daneben gibt es Hinweise auf den reifen Komponisten: der Einsatz von an Bach mahnendem Kontrapunkt, dissonante chromatische Reibungen zwischen erhöhten und erniedrigten Noten für realistische Wortmalerei sowie das langsame, marschartige Schreiten absteigender Basslinien.

Von dem *Requiem* da camera kam zu Finzis Lebzeiten nur das Vorspiel zur Aufführung. Es wurde am 1. Dezember 1925 von dem London Chamber Orchestra unter der Leitung von Anthony Bernard im Court House, Marylebone Lane, London mit Unterstützung der British Music Society gespielt. Philip Thomas' herausgegebene Fassung des gesamten Werkes einschließlich der vervollständigten Orchestrierung des dritten Satzes wurde am 7. Juni 1990 in der Christ Church, Spitalfields, London mit Stephen Varcoe (Bariton), den BBC Northern Singers und der City of London Sinfonia unter der Leitung von Richard Hickox uraufgeführt.

Die hier vorliegende Ausgabe und Vervollständigung von Christian Alexander wurde erstmals am 1. Dezember 2013 in der St Scholastica's Chapel, Glebe, New South Wales, Australien von dem Coro Innominata unter der Leitung von David Taylor interpretiert.

Andrew Burn, 2013

ANMERKUNG DES HERAUSGEBERS

Bei der Vorbereitung der hier vorliegenden, neuen praktischen Ausgabe von Finzis *Requiem da Camera* zog ich folgende Quellen heran:

(1) Finzis handschriftliche Partitur der Sätze I, II und IV (Faksimile)

(2) Finzis unvollständige Partitur des Satzes III (Faksimile: Bodleian Library, Ms. Mus. B. 33, Fol. 108–115)

(3) eine ältere handschriftliche Vertonung Finzis von *In Time of 'The Breaking of Nations'* für Gesang und Klavier (Faksimile: Bodleian Library, Ms. Mus. B. 33, Fol. 106–107)

(4) handschriftliche Bearbeitung des *Vorspiels* (*Requiem da Camera*) für Klavier zu vier Händen von Howard Ferguson (Handschrift eines Kopisten, Faksimile)

(5) handschriftlicher Klavierauszug, Sätze II, III und IV (Handschrift eines Kopisten, Faksimile)

Zu Finzis Lebzeiten kam nur das Vorspiel zur Aufführung. Das gesamte Werk dagegen wurde in Philip Thomas' Fassung von 1984 uraufgeführt und eingespielt. Finzi orchestrierte die Sätze I, II und IV vollständig. In diesen Abschnitten des *Requiems da Camera* war bei der Vorbereitung der hier vorliegenden Ausgabe nur sehr wenig redaktionelle Arbeit vonnöten. Eine solche Änderung geschah z. B. im zweiten Satz, Takt 58 (ein Takt vor Buchstabe D): Das Fes in Finzis Partitur scheint ein Fehler zu sein und wurde zu einem F korrigiert. Es soll auch darauf aufmerksam gemacht werden, dass der Tenor im Takt 69 des zweiten Satzes als letzte Note auf dem vierten Taktschlag ein Fis singt, wo in der Ausgabe von Philip Thomas ein F steht (so wie es auch in Richard Hickox' Einspielung erklingt). Finzis handschriftliche Partitur hat eine „Überklebung", die die Tonartenvorzeichen in der Tenorstimme nur auf dieser Seite verschwinden lässt. Zudem steht vor der fraglichen Note kein Auflösungszeichen und in dem handschriftlichen Klavierauszug eindeutig ein Fis. Ich glaube deshalb nicht, Finzi beabsichtigte, das Fis hier aufzulösen.

Im Vergleich zu diesen Eingriffen bedurfte der dritte Satz (*In Time of 'The Breaking of Nations'*) zur Vorbereitung auf eine Aufführung jedoch umfangreicherer redaktioneller Arbeit. Die ersten zwanzig Takte des dritten Satzes wurden von Finzi voll orchestriert. Allerdings waren auch hier einige redaktionelle Änderungen notwendig (meiner Meinung nach hätte Finzi zweifellos selbst Änderungen vorgenommen, wenn er die Musik zu einer Aufführung hätte vorbereiten müssen). Zu den von mir hier vorgenommenen Eingriffen gehören das Einfügen dynamischer Vortragsbezeichnungen, die Phrasierung, verdeutlichende Hinweise *divisi* in den Streichern und das Hinzufügen fehlender Vorzeichen. Im Takt 8 habe ich auch in der Hornstimme zwei Noten hinzugefügt, um einen Fehler in der zweiten Violinstimme in Finzis Partitur auszugleichen.

Ein weitaus stärkerer Eingriff war von Takt 21 bis zum Ende des dritten Satzes notwendig. Hier galt es, die Musik zu vervollständigen. Nichtsdestotrotz liefert Finzis unvollendete Partitur (besonders wenn man den konkreteren Klavierauszug vergleichend heranzieht) ausreichende Informationen, die die Absichten des Komponisten sehr deutlich werden lassen. Ich habe von der unvollendeten Partitur im Prinzip alles beibehalten und sie nur auf eine Weise ausgefüllt, wie Finzi es meiner Vorstellung nach getan hätte.

In meiner Ausgabe steht, die Gesangsstimmen sind mit vier Gesangssolisten oder kleinem Chor zu besetzen. Das bezieht sich auf den handschriftlichen Klavierauszug, der folgenden Hinweis gibt: „Die Gesangsstimmen sind für 4 Solisten: Sie können auch von einem kleinen ausgewogenen Chor von nicht mehr als 4 Sängern zu einer Stimme aufgeführt werden. In diesem Fall bietet es sich an, Streicher hinzuzufügen, maximal 4.4.3.3.2 und bei einem kleineren Chor entsprechend weniger. (Die 2. Kontrabassstimme sollte mit nicht weniger als dem Maximum besetzt werden.)"

Christian Alexander, Mai 2013
Übersetzung: Elke Hockings

Requiem da Camera

I – Prelude

II

How still this quiet cornfield is to-night!
By an intenser glow the evening falls,
Bringing, not darkness, but a deeper light;
Among the stooks a partridge covey calls.

The windows glitter on the distant hill;
Beyond the hedge the sheep-bells in the fold
Stumble on sudden music and are still;
The forlorn pinewoods droop above the wold.

An endless quiet valley reaches out
Past the blue hills into the evening sky;
Over the stubble, cawing, goes a rout
Of rooks from harvest, flagging as they fly.

So beautiful it is, I never saw
So great a beauty on these English fields,
Touched by the twilight's coming into awe,
Ripe to the soul and rich with summer's yields.

* * * * * * * * * * * *

These homes, this valley spread below me here,
The rooks, the tilted stacks, the beasts in pen,
Have been the heartfelt things, past-speaking dear
To unknown generations of dead men,

Who, century after century, held these farms,
And, looking out to watch the changing sky,
Heard, as we hear, the rumours and alarms
Of war at hand and danger pressing nigh.

And knew, as we know, that the message meant
The breaking off of ties, the loss of friends,
Death, like a miser getting in his rent,
And no new stones laid where the trackway ends.

The harvest not yet won, the empty bin,
The friendly horses taken from the stalls,
The fallow on the hill not yet brought in,
The cracks unplastered in the leaking walls.

[...]

Then sadly rose and left the well-loved Downs,
And so by ship to sea, and knew no more
The fields of home, the byres, the market towns,
Nor the dear outline of the English shore.

John Masefield (1878–1967), August, 1914 *(extract)*

Requiem da Camera

I – Prélude

II

Comme ce tranquille champ de maïs est calme ce soir!
Le jour tombe dans une lueur plus intense
Qui apporte, non pas l'obscurité, mais une lumière plus dense,
Au milieu des meulettes s'égosille une compagnie de perdrix.

Les fenêtres étincèlent sur la lointaine colline;
Au-delà de la haie, les cloches des brebis au bercail
S'entrechoquent en une soudaine musique puis se taisent;
Les pins solitaires s'inclinent au-dessus de la colline de craie.

Une vallée infinie et silencieuse s'étire
Par-delà les collines bleues vers le ciel du soir;
Au-dessus du chaume, passe en croassant, des champs moissonnés
Un vol de corbeaux pavoisant dans leur vol.

Tout est si magnifique que je n'ai jamais vu
De si grande beauté sur ces champs anglais,
Touchés par le crépuscule majestueux,
Mûrs jusqu'en leur âme et riches des récoltes d'été.

* * * * * * * * * * * *

Ces foyers, cette vallée étendue en dessous de moi,
Les corbeaux, les meules bâchées, les animaux rentrés,
Sont choses ressenties qui parlèrent chèrement
A des générations inconnues de disparus,

Qui, de siècles en siècles, ont tenu ces fermes,
Et, surveillant le ciel changeant,
Ont entendu, comme nous, les rumeurs et les alarmes
De la guerre proche et de l'imminence pressante du danger.

Et qui ont su, comme nous, que ce message annonçait
La rupture des liens, la perte des amis,
La mort, en avare récupérant sa rente,
Et aucune nouvelle pierre ajoutée au bout de la chaussée.

La moisson pas encore engrangée, la huche vide,
Le bon cheval arraché de l'écurie,
La jachère sur la colline pas même commencée,
Les fentes sans plâtrage des murs fissurés.

[...]

Puis, ils se sont levés tristement et on quitté leurs chers Downs,
Ont embarqué en mer, et n'ont plus reconnu
Les champs de chez eux, les étables, les villes de foire,
Ni le profil aimé des côtes de l'Angleterre.

John Masefield (1878–1967), *Août 1914* (extrait)

Requiem da Camera

I – Vorspiel

II

Wie ruhig das Feld heute Abend ist!
Der Abend neigt sich stark leuchtend,
bringt statt Dunkelheit ein tieferes Licht;
aus dem Heu ruft eine Schar Rebhühner.

Fenster glitzern auf dem fernen Hügel;
hinter der Hecke stolpern Schafsglocken
in ihrem Pferch plötzlich über Musik und sind ruhig;
auf der Weide ermatten die verlassenen Pinien.

Ein endloses, stilles Tal greift, vorbei an blauen Hügeln,
in den Abendhimmel;
über die Stoppeln kommt krächzend eine Bande Krähen
von der Ernte und flattert beim Abflug.

Es ist so schön, nie sah ich
eine größere Schönheit auf englischen Feldern,
ehrfürchtig berührt von der Abenddämmerung,
reif bis ins Tiefste, und reich an der Ausbeute des Sommers.

* * * * * * * * * * * * *

Die Häuser und Täler breiten sich hier vor mir aus,
die Krähen, die schiefen Heustapel, die eingesperrten Tiere,
waren die tiefempfundenen Dinge, die in der Vergangenheit liebevoll
zu Generationen unbekannter, toter Männer sprachen,

Die, Jahrhundert nach Jahrhundert, diese Farmen hielten,
und die, während sie nach dem Wechsel des Himmels schauten,
so wie wir die Gerüchte und Alarme eines nahen Krieges
und drohender Gefahr hörten.

Und die, wie wir, wussten, dass diese Nachricht
den Bruch von Bindungen, den Verlust von Freunden bedeutete,
und Tod, wie ein Geizhals seine Miete fordernd;
und dass dort wo der Weg endet, keine neuen Steine gelegt würden.

Die Ernte noch nicht eingefahren, der Speicher leer,
die freundlichen Pferde aus dem Stall geholt,
das Brachland auf dem Hügel noch nicht bearbeitet,
die Risse in den lecken Wänden nicht verputzt.

[...]

Erhob mich traurig und verließ die geliebte Heimat,
fuhr mit dem Schiff zur See, und kannte die heimischen Felde nicht mehr,
die Ställe, die Marktstädte,
auch nicht die Kontur der geliebten englischen Küste.

John Masefield (1878–1967), *August, 1914 (Auszug)*

III

Only a man harrowing clods
In a slow silent walk
With an old horse that stumbles and nods
Hálf asleep as they stalk.

Only thin smoke without flame
From the heaps of couch-grass;
Yet this will go onward the same
Though Dynasties pass.

Yonder a maid and her wight
Come whispering by:
War's annals will cloud into night
Ere their story die.

Thomas Hardy (1840–1928),
In Time of 'The Breaking of Nations'

IV

We who are left, how shall we look again
Happily on the sun or feel the rain,
Without remembering how they who went
Ungrudgingly, and spent
Their lives for us, loved too the sun and the rain?

A bird among the rain-wet lilac sings—
But we, how shall we turn to little things
And listen to the birds and winds and streams
Made holy by their dreams,
Nor feel the heart-break in the heart of things?

Wilfrid Wilson Gibson (1878–1962), Lament

III

Seul, un homme herse les mottes
Dans le silence d'une marche lente
Avec un vieux cheval qui trébuche et dodeline
Endormi à demi alors qu'ils avancent.

Seule, une fine fumée sans flamme
S'échappe des tas de chiendent ;
Et tout ceci demeurera inchangé
Tandis que passeront les Dynasties.

Là-bas une jeune fille et son pauvre hère
Passent en chuchotant :
Les chroniques de guerre vont obscurcir la nuit
Avant que ne s'achève leur histoire.

Thomas Hardy (1840–1928),
À l'heure de 'la rupture des nations'

IV

Pour nous qui restons, comment regarder encore
Avec bonheur le soleil ou sentir la pluie,
Sans nous souvenir que ceux qui partirent
De bon cœur et consumèrent
Leur vies pour nous, aimèrent aussi le soleil et la pluie ?

Un oiseau chante dans le lilas mouillé de pluie—
Mais nous, comment nous tourner vers les petites choses,
Ecouter les oiseaux, les vents et les ruisseaux
Sanctifiés par leurs rêves,
Et ne pas ressentir le cœur brisé des choses ?

Wilfrid Wilson Gibson (1878–1962), *Lamentation*
Traduction : Agnès Ausseur

III

Nur ein Mann, der langsam und leise
die Erde für die Saat bereitet
mit einem alten Pferd, stolpernd und nickend,
im Halbschlaf voranschreitend.

Nur dünner Rauch, keine Flamme,
aus den Quecken-Haufen;
doch dies wird immer, durch alle Dynastien,
so weitergehen.

Dort drüben eine Maid und ihr Mann,
flüsternd vorübergehend:
die Annalen des Krieges werden im Himmel sich trüben
bevor ihre Geschichten versterben.

Thomas Hardy (1840–1928),
In Zeiten zerbrechender Nationen

IV

Wir, die wir übrig sind, wie sollen wir je wieder
glücklich die Sonne anblicken oder den Regen spüren,
ohne uns zu erinnern, wie auch die, die bereitwillig loszogen
und ihr Leben für uns ließen,
auch die Sonne und den Regen liebten?

Ein Vogel singt auf regennassem Flieder—
aber wir, wie sollen wir uns den kleinen Dingen zuwenden,
und den Vögeln, den Winden, und Bächen lauschen
durch ihre Träume gesegnet
und dabei nicht den Kummer im Herzen der Dinge spüren?

Wilfrid Wilson Gibson (1878–1962), *Wehklage*
Übersetzung: Heike Römer

Scoring

Baritone Solo★
Small Chorus★

Flute
Oboe
Cor anglais
Clarinet in B♭ (doubling Bass Clarinet)
Horn in F
Harp
Strings

★or four solo voices

Duration: 24 minutes

On sale:

Study score
Organ reduction by Francis Jackson
Prelude, arranged for piano duet by Howard Ferguson

Performance materials available on hire

In memory of E. B. F.

REQUIEM DA CAMERA

I – Prelude
TACET

GERALD FINZI
Completed by
CHRISTIAN ALEXANDER

II

Words by
JOHN MASEFIELD
(1878–1967)

19459

droop a - bove the wold.

droop a - bove the wold.

rit

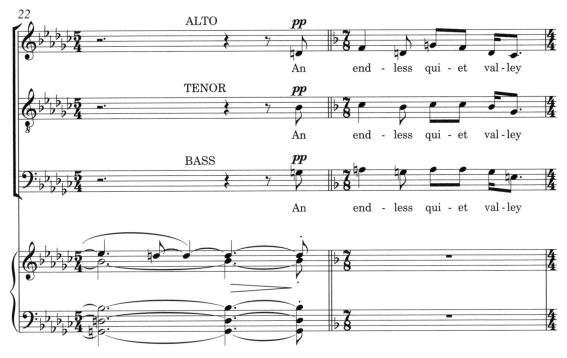

ALTO
An end - less qui - et val - ley

TENOR
An end - less qui - et val - ley

BASS
An end - less qui - et val - ley

4

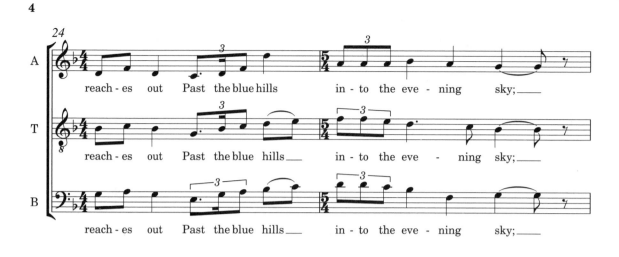

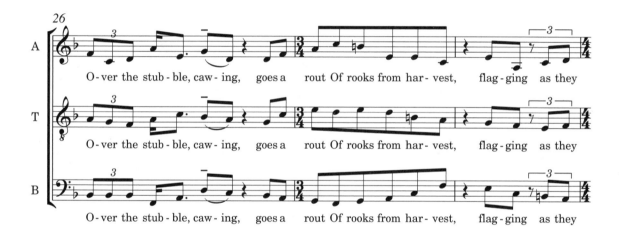

Words by
THOMAS HARDY
(1840–1928)

III

stalk.

On - ly thin smoke___ with - out flame_____ From the

heaps_____ of couch-grass;_____ Yet this_

_____ will go on-ward the same Though Dy-nas-ties pass._____

Yon - der   a maid   and her   wight   Come

whis-per - ing   by:_____   War's   an-nals   will

cloud   in - to   night_____   Ere

their sto - - ry die.

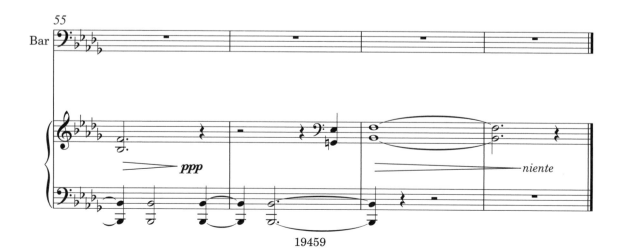

Words by
WILFRID WILSON GIBSON
(1878–1962)

IV

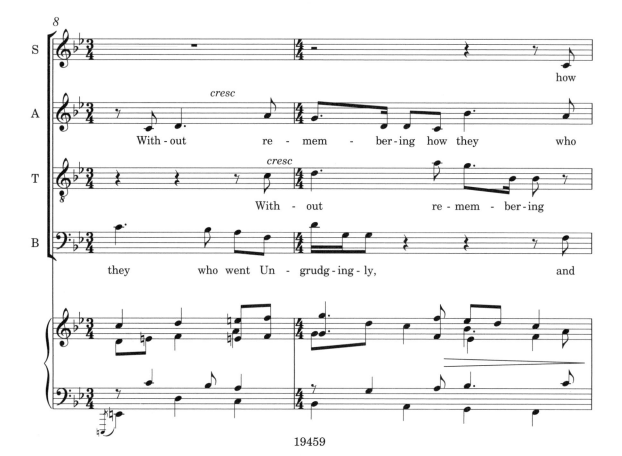

★ When there is a chorus

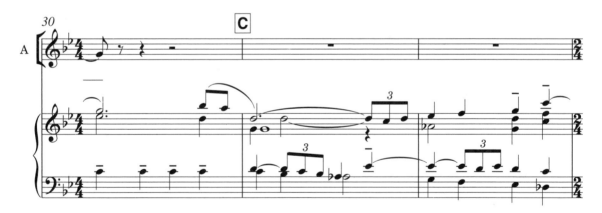

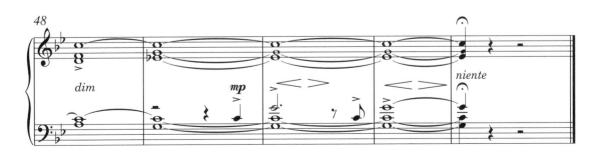